Coyote's Bones

Selected Poetry and Prose of

Jaime de Angulo

EDITED BY BOB CALLAHAN

TURTLE ISLAND FOUNDATION
SAN FRANCISCO 1974

Coyote's Bones is the fourth volume of the
Jaime de Angulo Library.

Copyright © 1974 by Turtle Island Foundation

Acknowledgement is made to the editors of *The In-
dependent*, *Laughing Horse* and *Nine* where some of
these stories and poems first appeared.

Special thanks to Will C. Jumper, Bard Norville,
Robert Duncan and Gui de Angulo for locating some
of this material.

Library of Congress Catalog Card Number: 73-78141

Turtle Island Foundation
2907 Bush Street, San Francisco California 94115

Don Gregorio Sketches

Lorca Translations

Indios

Coyote's Bones

Preface

There is in Paris, near the Trocadero, a wonderful museum—it contains a magnificent collection of statues, paintings, books, 3 floors of them all devoted to the religions—a gift to the nation from Emile Guimet, industrialist, chemist, writer, who collected them in his travels of research in Asia, China, Japan Thibet, Indo-China, etc. He was interested also in the mythologies of Assyria, Babylonia, Egypt, Greece. He is the author of many scholarly works. (1836-1871)

My family lived not far from there, and as a child around the age of ten I spent many an afternoon in my beloved Musee Guimet. I gained the friendship of a guardian, a queer type who had educated his own self in the museum's library. He let me borrow many books. That's how I discovered to my great relief that not all religions were as flat, as absurd, as dead and boring as the Catholicism of my people. That was the beginning of my rebellion.

Don Gregorio Sketches

Don Gregorio & the Straw Hat

That summer we were vacationing in Trouville, which in those days of the mid 90s was a fashionable seaside resort. My father's current fad at that time was the *Kneip Cure*, which enjoyed a great vogue in those days among the devotees of health and rational living. One of the tenets of the Cure was to eat slowly and chew the food thoroly—in fact you shud masticate every morsel no less than a dozen times before swallowing it. My father took this, as everything else, literally; there he sat at his meal, with his head turned sideways to the open book of the moment, conscientiously masticating each piece *twelve* times. He ate alone, and his meal lasted from five to seven o'clock. The rest of the family, my mother, my sister, my brother and i, trooped in at six o'clock and were finished by half past six. My father was never able to make any of us masticate properly, altho he tried.

Another tenet of the Cure was to walk *barefoot* in the grass before the morning dew had evaporated. This, my father did every morning. Both he and i were early risers, always up at dawn (i was about six or seven, then). So we sallied forth, both barefoot, and walked a mile or so out of town to where there were some lush green cow pastures, he walking ahead with his long strides and i trotting behind like a faithful dog.

My father never wore a hat. In those days a hat was as necessary a part of a man's costume as were his trousers, and to go about bareheaded was as unusual as to go about without his pants, and almost as shocking. But my father cared not a fig for public opinion (to which he referred, contemptuously, as *la vanidad mundana*); he did not affront it; he did not ignore it; he simply did not see it. He never realized that he was an odd, an eccentric character. But my poor mother did! Dona Ysabel was a paragon of conventional correction (or maybe we thot so because of the contrast with Don Gregorio?).

That summer, however, my father was much bothered by the glare of sunlight; and on that particular morning, as we were returning on bare feet from those dewey meadows, he made an important decision: he wud buy a straw hat!

So, we turned into the town in quest of a hat-shop. The morning was just getting along and people were leisurely shopping here and there. We found a hat shop and went in. There was a demoiselle behind the counter and my father explained in his grammatically correct but atrociously pronounced French that he desired a straw hat with a very wide brim. The demoiselle smiled and said "Oui, Monsieur, certainement" and disappeared and soon returned with several trim *canotiers*, those stiff little hats they used to wear in the summer in Europe and in New York but i never saw one in the West. My father's face fell. No, no, no, he cried, that was not at all what he wanted (and indeed, he wud have been a figure of fun in one of the little monkey hats, he with his prophet's face and flowing beard!). He wanted a hat with a large brim, a very wide brim.

So the demoiselle went back and returned with some more canotiers . . . the brim of these was surely all of a quarter-inch broader, in fact they were daringly wide brimmed . . . Just then, my father's eye lit on a pile of gardener's hats put away on a top shelf. "Ha!" he exclaimed triumphantly, that was what he wanted.

The demoiselle's eyes were wide with horror. "Mais, Monsieur, ce sont des chapeaux de jardinier!" (Now, observe: she said they were gardener's hats, not garden hats. A tremendous difference in social classification!) My father's answer was "It is all equal to me! I want one of those hats! Give me one of those hats!" She climbed on a short ladder and she brot them down. I thot she was going to burst into tears. As a final plea to my father to be reasonable, she said: "But Sir, they cost only six pennies." "Eh bien, tant mieux! all the better!" said my father and he crowned himself with a gardener's hat. He really did not look bad at all in it. It fitted his noble face. The demoiselle's look of on-the-verge of tears changed to a slightly admiring one. But my father's eternal utilitarianism had to spoil the picture again. He demanded to have ribbons sewed on to the hat so he cud tie them under his chin against the wind. Now the demoiselle's smile changed to plain laughter. She

5

rummaged under the counter and produced scissors, needle and thread, and a wide red ribbon. In a few deft movements she had two ribbons sewed on to the hat; my father crowned himself again; and she herself tied the scarlet bow-knot under his beard. She was laughing. Her laughter did not at all annoy my father. He simply remarked to me: "Pero, que amable es!" And we sallied forth into the street, my father barefoot and with his new hat, and me trotting behind him.

We were now going home, and there were quite a few people on the streets. Just then, coming in our direction, but on the other side of the street, we saw my mother. Dona Ysabel was short and somewhat corpulent; tightly laced in her corsets and wearing very high heels; she always dressed carefully in the correct mode of the day, but without any ostentation. So there she came as usual walking very erect with her short steps, holding her train in one hand and her parasol in the other. As i said, we saw her; *and she saw us at the very same instant.* She stopped abruptly for perhaps five seconds. Then she whirled around, and fled up the street.

"Ysabel! Eh . . . YSABEL!!!" my father yelled in stentorian tones, taking long strides.

Passers-by stopped and turned around, staring, and shopkeepers came to their doorsteps. "Ysabel, Eh, Ysa-BEL!!" But Dona Ysabel was fleeing up the street, almost at a run. At the corner she turned into another street. My father stopped. He turned to me. "Pero, que le pasa, esta loco?" (What is the matter with her? is she crazy?).

6

Don Gregorio & his Chronometer

My father had always had a passion for watches. Yes, a passion! not just an interest, but a passion. Shortly before his death when after 20 yrs. of estrangement I had decided it was stupid on my part to continue the feud, and went and made my submission he said: "I don't remember when this passion started . . . it must have been during my childhood . . . the idea that you could, so to speak, materialize time (that most immaterial thing) and metamorfoze it into a maze of wheels inside a little box. . . ."

He kept his watches as other people keep a stable of horses. Usually, watch fanciers are interested in the face of the watch, its style, Ier. Empire, Restoration, Rococo, etc. They keep those watches under cloche and let them run down. Not so with Don Gregorio. He had about three score watches and *they all ran!* He kept them in a closet with shelves. If you were not forwarned and opened the door of the closet you almost fell over backward! Such a racket! Such a tintamarre! Sixty watches ticking at the same time!

Then, on every floor of our villa in La Baule there was one or two of those horloges bretonnes, 6ft. tall. They had a pendulum and a couple of weights. You wound the weights every two weeks. Those were very ornamental clocks. But Don Gregorio did not care a rap about that. The looks of a clock did not interest him; what he wanted was that it shud give the time properly.

But the king of them all was THE chronometer. It was a marine chronometer, one of those things in a box about a foot square, and hung so that it was always level. It had been made by Leroy-Beaulieu, the great chronometer-maker of the Bould. de la Madeleine. Don Gregorio had paid a fortune for it! Naturally, you never changed it. You simply calculated each time the amount it had gained or lost. A good chronometer does not vary more than seven seconds a day. But the really important thing is that it should vary (either advance or retard) a regular amount. A chronometer which gains a second one day, then three the next, then retards one second the next day, is not a good chronometer; too temperamental!

In those days before wireless, my father got the *right* time from the Navy, at Saint-Nazaire some 20 kilometers from La Baule. My father made the trip every 2 weeks, by train, just to obtain the right time. He carried in his sack a small quasi-chronometer and this he put in accord with the Chronomètre de la Marine. He always went alone except that I accompanied him. I adored my father the way one adores God. If I had had my way I wud never have left his side. He never even noticed my presence, and he never said anything to me. He was one of the most silent men I have ever known; at least in those days he was.

I pause here a moment for a query: *why* was Don G. so much in love with watches? As I have said already,

8

it was not the artistic value of the watch; that left him completely indifferent. Neither was it the *collector's instinct*. My father collected many items that usually go into collections; at various times he collected lenses, pictures, rocks, meteorites (that was when we were in the Pyrénées—and the peasants, the montagnards, collected them in the high mountains and then sold them to the tourists—but always after breaking them in half to show the beautiful shining structure of the metal—to my father this was sacrilege! he wud buy none of those, to the amazement of the peasants—he tried vainly to explain to them that these ugly objects came *from another planet than* the earth, they came from outer space—mais vas donc leur faire comprendre, ces pauvres imbéciles! They looked at my father with suspicion). He collected moorish plates. Postage-stamps are the only thing he never collected, strangely enuf! So, Don Gregorio *did* have the instinct of a collector, there is no denying it. Yet i was certain, even far back in the days of my childhood that the collector's instinct had nothing to do with it. I was puzzled—and I did not understand it until years later, just before his death.

So i quarreled with him and came to America and had no more communication with him until years later when i realized that i was acting like a fool and went back and made my submission, and he died happy.

Now, the story of my father, his valet-de-chambre and the chronometer happened some ten years later, during the First World War. (I volunteered in the medical corps, 1st Lieut. and spent the next 18 months

9

trying to find out *where i was supposed to be!* The Army had misplaced my papers. It's incredible but it is so!) So, i never was present at the "Affaire du Chronometre." All I know is what my Sister told me.

Altho my father hardly ever spoke to anyone his figure was well-known in the country-side where he took long rides on his bicycle. They thot he was a sort of madman, but quite harmless. "Le millionaire espagnol" they called him. Somehow or other the idea had entered his head that he had been appointed official timekeeper for the county. He had taken it upon himself to care for the great church clock on the main square of the town. He had also taken charge of the clock at the railway-station. And whenever he met someone in uniform, the postman maybe, or a gardechampêtre, he offered to give them the correct time. The transaction was a silent one—no words wasted. Don Gregorio took his watch out of his pocket and the other person did the same. They compared the watches side-by-side; the small error, if there was one, was corrected and each man went his way, smiling.

All this was before the days of the radio. The radio changed Don Gregorio's life. No longer necessary, those bi-weekly trips to Saint Nazaire to get the proper time at the Bureau de la Marine. Now he cud have the correct time *twice* a day, at noon and at midnight. Incredible! Life was good.

The war! and the American troops occupied Brittany and went joyously at the game of teaching the Frogs the ways of the superior life. All private radios were, of course, ordered dismantled. But now that he had tasted the intoxicating thing, he cud not face going back to the old life. *He decided to take a chance!* He would keep his antenna. Nobody wud notice. The childish lack of appreciation of reality is appalling! It also showed an appalling lack of understanding of war and the military mind. Because he was so certain of his honesty he thot that honesty wud immediately become apparent to the others. My sister was in tears!

It did not take the occupying Americans long to discover my father's radio, and they demanded Don Gregorio's arrest as a spy. In vain did the French authorities plead with the American commander. "The man is well-known to us—absolutely harmless—just a crackpot—." The American was obdurate.

Now things began to move fast—everybody moved fast except Don Gregorio. He was sublimely ignorant of the danger. He had done no wrong, he was quite serene. But it was the hour of his lunch when they came to arrest him, and he refused to move until he had had his lunch. In vain the Commissaire de Police appealed to him. "Monsieur, je vous en prie, pressez-vous, pressez-vous, vous n'avez pas l'air de comprendre la situation. Vous entendez ces cris, dehors? Eh bien c'est la foule en émeute. Vous n'avez probablement jamais vu une foule en émeute. Moi, c'est mon métier. Ce sont de braves gens qui tout à coup deviennent des bêtes-en-fureur."

My sister told me that it was one of the most terrible moments of her life. "Figurez-vous cette foule, d'ordinaire de bons paysans, des commercants polis, des voisins aimables. Et tous hurlaient 'A mort l'espion!

L'espagnol à la lanterne, l'espagnol à la lanterne!"And between them and the grille of the garden, some twenty mounted policemen with slung carbines. In the salle-à-manger Don Gregorio eating an omelette with perfect unconcern, served by the butler in civvies (they had arrested him as accomplice).

Finally the omelette was finished and the three of them descended the stairs and entered the police wagon. The mounted policemen quickly formed an escort around the wagon, and off they went for the railroad station. The way led past the Place de l'Eglise. The Commissaire told my sister that Don Gregorio begged them to stop so he cud put the big clock on time.

The Americans kept Don Gregorio and the butler in jail for a whole month before they were convinced of his innocence. Don Gregorio and the butler had to share the same cell. Don Gregorio kept up a jeremiad of self-accusatory acts of contrition. It was God punishing him, and that sort of thing. Eugène at first assented:"Oui Monsieur, oui monsieur." Then he became surly and did not open his mouth any more. Then one day, in the midst of a jeremiad he got up deliberately from his cot, he bent over and took hold of the pot-de-chambre in both hands, and he stood over Don Gregorio: "Un mot de plus . . . et je vous mets la tête en bouillie!" My father yelled: "Au secours. 'il est devenu fou!" After that they were put in two separate cells.

Years later, when I visited him and my sister, i found them in the Basque country, on the French side.

He had changed very much, of course, mellowed. My sister explained to me that she could not bear living in La Baule after the trouble. The place has become odious to her. "Je n'oublierai jamais le cauchemar de cette foule hurlant 'A mort l'espion! l'espagnol à la lanterne!' Ces têtes défigurées par la cruauté, par une passion obscène!" She had sold the house for a song and they had come here to the lovely pays basque.

One evening, my father and I sat outside smoking. The night was warm and clear, and the stars brilliant. My father began telling me how he had managed to get the right time before private radios were allowed again. He had made friends with one of the French priests at a local astronomical observatory. He had learned to calculate "sideral time" by making observations on the stars. And with emotion choking his voice he told me how he had discovered a new world! "Just think, just think about the speed of light, 200,000 kilometers per second!" His voice had dropped to a murmur. He began to tell me about the wonders of modern physics. Then he told me how time was only one of the four coordinates of matter . . . *Then it was that I understood his passion for watches.*

The night-chill entered into us and we went indoors. It was almost midnight and time for the broadcast of the time from the Eiffel tower. And while we waited for it a strange expression came over his face. "The Jesuits wanted me to study law! I never understood the law! For me it was only a jumble of illogicalities, a senseless galimatias! Just suppose they had let me learn physics and chemistry, biology—I might have

13

become a great scientist! But Spain is a barbarous country!" and while he was saying that, a wave of bitterness was swelling inside myself. I wanted to say: "Yes, and you my father kept me in schools of jesuits where we were forbidden to read books on physics and chemistry, and biology!" but I did not say it.

Pretty soon the signals began coming in. The large room was very dimly lit by an oil-lamp, one of those things in the Pyrénées that have not changed since roman times. You still find them in use. It looks like half of an avocado pear, with a wick which dips in the oil (olive oil was so cheap in those days!). The wick hangs outside and it gives out a soft yellow light. The room was full of dancing shadows.

Now the signals were coming fast and Don G. was entering them in notebooks for the several chronometers (of the 2nd class), and to his horror one of them that he was especially interested in had gone on a rampage! It was several seconds off (we discovered the next day that it was my father who had made a mistake!).

I started for my room and turned around to say good-night. My father was sitting in his chair, a picture of desolation. He held the chronometer in his hand and was shaking his head slowly, from side to side. He was saying in an injured tone: "Ay, tu, bribon! bribon!" (oh, you, scoundrel, scoundrel!").

Marceline, Vous Etes Une Cochonne!

For some reason my mother nursed me herself. Just the same, when i was born they sent for a nurse, a "dry nurse." This was Marceline, and she stayed with us until i was six, when she went back to her "pays"; she came from central France.

Marceline was a typical peasant: obdurate, stupid, slow (my father nicknamed her Culo-de-Plomo). Naturally she became devoted to me and i became devoted to her. In a sense, she was "mother" to me much more than my mother. Yet, note this point: she addressed me as "Monsieur Jaime," never as plain Jaime; and of course, she used the "Vous."

I can see us going out after lunch, my sister aged 9, my brother 7, and myself 4, all in charge of Marceline. We go up the Champs-Elysees, around the Arc-de-Triomphe, then we enter the Avenue du Bois (de Boulogne), and before we have gone very far we find some of our "gang" (my sister and my brother are always the leaders, everywhere, it is they who organize games); i hate children, so i stay with "Culo-de-Plomo" who has joined the other bonnes d'enfants on a bench, i play by myself making sand-pies.

Now, for a long time i had been wondering about the jets d'eau of the Place de la Concorde. *What made the water go up?* i used to wonder and wonder and wonder.

i lay in bed at night imagining a complicated system of paddle wheels each one throwing some water up to the paddle above, and so on and on. But i knew intuitively that there was something simpler than that!

i asked Marceline. She said she did not know. i insisted that she did. "Tell me, tell me! i want you to tell me!!" I got myself into a fury. i stamped my foot. I yelled "Marceline, vous êtes une cochonne!!" to which she replied with calm: "Je le sais. Vous me l'avez dejà dit! . . . vous êtes une vieille cochonne!!"

How that problem of artesian water worried me.

It was 2 or 3 years later that i understood, partly. i was playing in the pantry. i had let the water half fill the sink and i was doing something with a little boat i had carved. i don't remember what it was that i was doing but it involved a long rubber tube. Anyway, at a certain moment i let the end of the tube drop; the tube had been full of water, and one end of it was still in the sink. i saw the water run out of the other end onto the floor of the pantry and i expected that all the water already inside the tube would thus run out, but to my amazement the water *continued* to run out . . . and more, and more . . . and more until *all* the water in the sink had been siphoned out!

We soon heard from the people in the apartment below: their ceiling was leaking! Hulaballoo!! the concierge was there in no time, and the servants from below, and my mother and my brother and sister. They were all trying to find out from me what it was that i was trying to do. But i was like one in a trance! i knew confusedly in my mind that there was the answer to my great puzzle; what made the water go up. I cudn't work it out but somehow, intuitively, i knew that the two phenomena were connected, the jets d'eau of the Place de la Concorde and the water siphoned out of the sink.

I was angry, i felt cheated. Why didn't they explain important things to little boys?!!

Yes, i was angry, i thot to myself: "yes, at school you fill me up with stupid stories, with arguments about sin, about the state of grace, all sorts of things which bore me, things which I don't understand (and which, i suspect, you do not understand either)! Meanwhile you let a miracle, a real miracle, go bye, and you do not tell me! a miracle which makes me dance with joy, the miracle of communicating vases, the miracle of water going up-hill! Either you have no imagination, or you are very stupid."

Yes, i was angry; i felt cheated; i felt they had let me down. And i wanted to shout: "Vous êtes des cochons! vous êtes des cochons!" i was around 8 or 9. i made my final rebellion when i was just turned 12. i remember that date because it was when I made my "first communion"—a gala day for most boys, but for me a day of disillusion, a day of bitterness. The whole thing, then, was a farce. i cud no longer believe my parents, my teachers. i was on my own; if there is a Truth then i must find it by myself—i was alone, and i was scared. Six long years of loneliness, of bitterness, of doubt—until i broke away and came to America.

A Letter to Ezra and Dorothy Pound

Dear Ezra & Dorothy

Beatrice Abbots is quite right abaut the importance of the pineal gland. I myself hav made a lifelong study of the pineal and also of the infra-renal glands. And also she iz quite right about the habits of sheep and sheepherders. I am an expert on sheepherders—no, I myself never herded sheep, but I was a cow-boy, and cow-boys know all about sheepherders. Let me tell you what happened to me once back in 1904; I was a raw lad of 18 with no more education than what I cud get at a couple of Jesuit colleges in Paris, and I was expelled from both sine laude whatever—so I came to Amerika bekoz I was thirsting for democracy and took a job with the Two Bar outfit and their small herd of 22,000 head of catl grazing here and ther on the mountains and bad lands of northern Colorado and southern Wyoming—I was a night-hawk, a lonesome job which gave me plenty of time to reflect on democracy and the pineal gland—(the night-hawk herds the saddle-horses (about a hundred horses—i had 98 on that trip, in my remuda) when the outfit (one boss, six or seven punchers, one cook, one day-wrangler, one night-wrangler .... whom they call the "night-hawk"—and it's a darn lonesome job riding round and round the

dam critters all night and singing so they wont get
scared and stampede and the sagebrush looks weird in
the moonlight and the night-hawks, i mean the real
ones, the birds, come plummeting down out of the
darkness overhead and they straighten out just over
your head with a whooosh that's enuf to scare the
pineal gland out of the bravest jesuit-bred lad of 18
.... wel, to shorten this account of this my first experi-
ence with sheepherders one night a goddam sheep got
mixed-up with my caballada, of cors they stampeded
every time they saw that goddam ghostly animal ap-
pear from behind a bush ... off they wud go ratapala-
planking thru the sage and I after them and you are
lucky if your horse doesnt put his foot in a badger-hole
and it breaks his leg and the rider's head and good-bye
pineal! wel, the dawn came at last with the most lovly
of all planets the morning-star and that's the time to
gather the horses and go home to the camp where the
punchers are crawling out from under their tarpaulins
... wel i started my horses and there on the plain in the
first light of dawn I saw a sheepherder's camp, so I
went over, and there were six or seven thousand head
of bawling sheep, and a sheepherder's wagon, and in
front of it was standing the sheepherder himself, enjoy-
ing the dawn smoking a pipe, but he didn't look like no
sheperd of the Lord, he didnt hav no lamb wrapped
around his neck, in fact he was quite a surprising sight
in that far-western land: he wore bib-overalls (i had
never seen any before) no shoes, and a derby hat and he
was bearded, but I mean bearded, a real beard with
crumbs in it ... so i went up to him and sed: "I guess you

lost a sheep last night" he looked at me and replied: "I guess you lost a sheep last night" I sed: "hell no, I am no sheepherder" he looked at me and sed: "hell no, I am no sheepherder" I sd: "You are no sheepherder? then what's all these animals here?" he repeated that too . . . . wel i thot the conversation was not profitable so I left him there contemplating the sunset and to hell with his lost sheep nobody wud miss one sheep in seven thousand and i went to camp with my horses and the cow-boys sed I was lucky he didn't shoot me, that shepe didnt like cowboys . . . . well, it was much later when I was studying psychiatry at the Hopkins that i learned about echolalia and i remembered my sheepherder and I wud hav done anything to find him again and see whether he cud spell bekoz by that time I had discovered that bad spelling was a minor symptom of ecolalia especially when it gets complicated with the retroversion-retroflex of the infrarenal glands (and by the way, did ennibodi at St Lizzy take radiogramz of Ezra's infrarenals? I bet that's why he kant spel my own kase has nothing to do with it, my bad speling iz due to an entirely difrent cause . . . mine is due to derangement of the Russian gland . . . I know what you will sat that ther iz no such thing az the Russian gland but there iz only it's hard to locate because it wanders, it's a wandering gland, that's why Mrs. Roosevelt has found out, now the secret is out, but I trust you, and dont let anybody, especially not Vishinsky know that I know about the Russian gland, or I'll get murdered some day).

Love,
Jaime

Lorca
Translations

LANDSCAPE

The field
of olive-trees
opens and closes
like a fan.
The sky is sombre
over the olive-grove
with a dark rain
of cold stars.
By the river-bank in penumbra
the reeds tremble.
There are grey curls in the air.
The olive-trees
are heavy
with lament.
A flock
of captive birds
trailing forever
their long tails in the shadow.

SOLEÁ

Dressed in black shawls
she thinks the world is small
and the heart immense.

Dressed in black shawls.

She thinks that both the tender sigh
and the shriek
disappear in the wind.

Dressed in black shawls.

She left the window open
and through the window the dawn
poured in with all heaven.

Ay yayayayay . . .
all dressed up in black shawls!

ARCHERS

The shadowy archers
approaching Sevilla.

—Guadalquivir wide open—

Wide grey sombreros
and long slow capas.

—!Ay, Guadalquivir!—

Coming from the far-away
countries of pain.

—Guadalquivir wide open—

They enter a labyrinth.
Love, crystal and rock.

—!Ay, Guadalquivir!—

After Passing

The children are looking
at something far away.

The candles are put out.
Some blind girls
are questioning the moon,
and through the air
a wail rises in spirals

The mountains are looking
at something far away.

The Cry

The ellipse of a cry
travels from mount
to mount.

From the olive-trees,
like a rainbow black
in the blue of night.

      Ay!

Like the bow to a viol
the cry sets long vibrations
in the cords of the wind.

      Ay!

The people of the caves
show up with their lanterns.

NIGHT

Candle, lamp,
lantern, and firefly.

The constellation
of the dart.

Little windows of gold
trembling,
and cross upon cross
rocking in the dawn.

Candle, lamp,
lantern and firefly.